GAMES & Puzzles

FEATURING PAT'S PATENT PENDING

CODE LETTER™ SCRAMBLES

Use the Code Letter icons to help unscramble the mixed-up letters to spell common words.

HOW DO YOU RANK?

Zero completed = F	Six completed = B+
One or two completed = D	Seven completed = A-
Three or four completed = C	Eight completed = A
Five completed = B	Nine completed = A+

ANSWERS: Each puzzle is numbered. Answers are located at the back of the book.

Dalmatian Press

Printed in Ft. Wayne, IN, U.S.A.
The **DALMATIAN PRESS** name and logo are trademarks of Dalmatian Publishing Group, Franklin, TN 37067. 1-866-418-2572.

CE14372/0811

PAT SAJAK'S

GAMES & Puzzles

FEATURING PAT'S PATENT PENDING

CODE LETTER SCRAMBLES

INSTRUCTIONS:
The code icons help identify letters in these mixed-up common words. Once you figure out a Code Letter, write the letter in each coded square of the 9 words.

#1 NOUIN

#2 DYELO

#3 LOWEH

#4 YRDBIH

#5 HBEROT

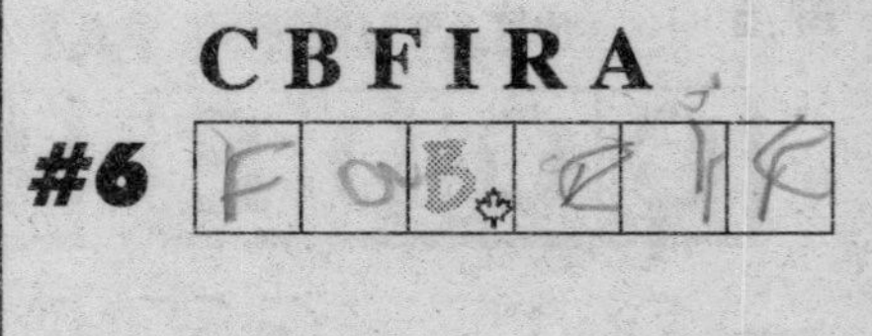

#6 CBFIRA

#7 LHUILP

#8 TLEESN

#9 BARDVE

PAT SAJAK'S

GAMES & Puzzles

FEATURING PAT'S PATENT PENDING

CODE LETTER SCRAMBLES

#1 STPNA

#2 UEBSL

#3 PTRBUA

#4 UONATM

#5 DLBEIR

#6 AECMAR

#7 NGRJOA

#8 HECNSO

#9 GEMANL

PAT SAJAK'S

GAMES & Puzzles

FEATURING PAT'S PATENT PENDING

CODE LETTER SCRAMBLES

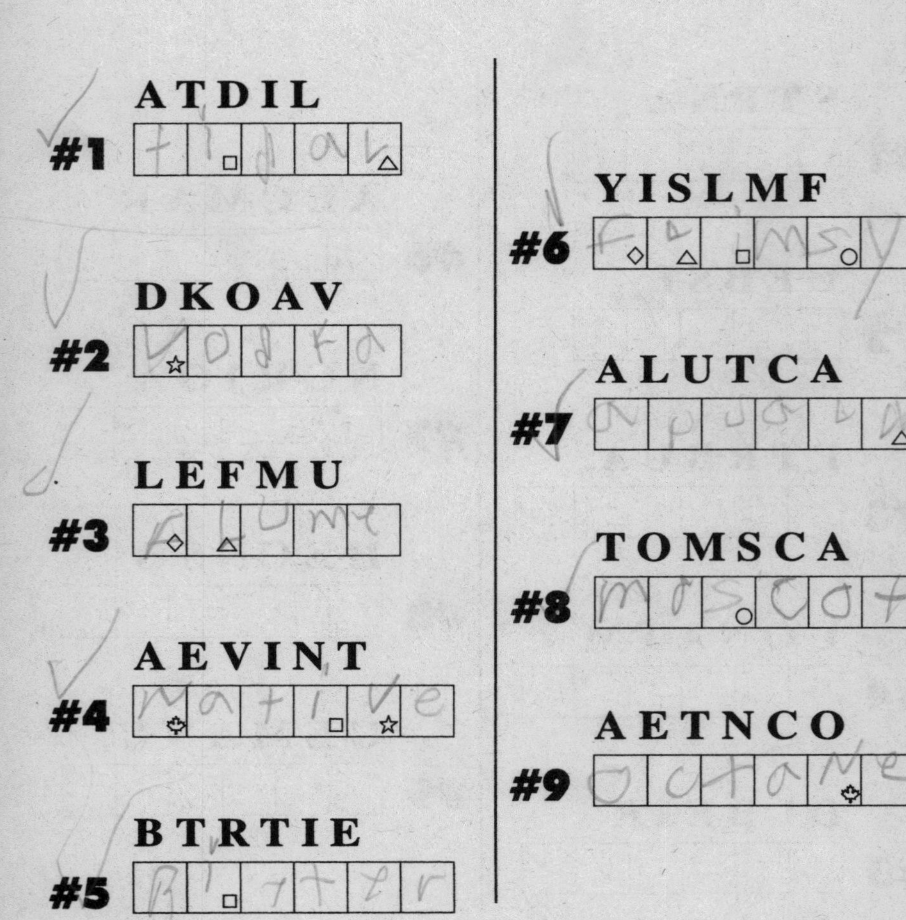

PAT SAJAK'S

GAMES & Puzzles

FEATURING PAT'S PATENT PENDING

CODE LETTER SCRAMBLES

N W N K O

#1

U A S B C

#2 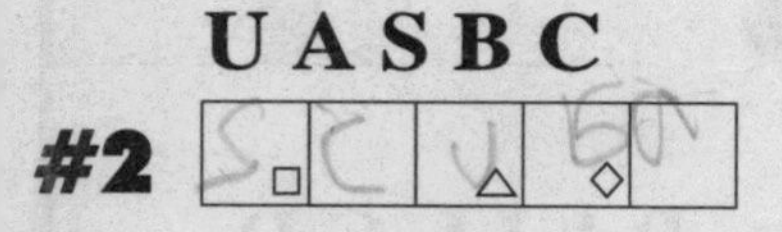

R O M N O

#3 

L M A O R N

#4 

T M S I F I

#5 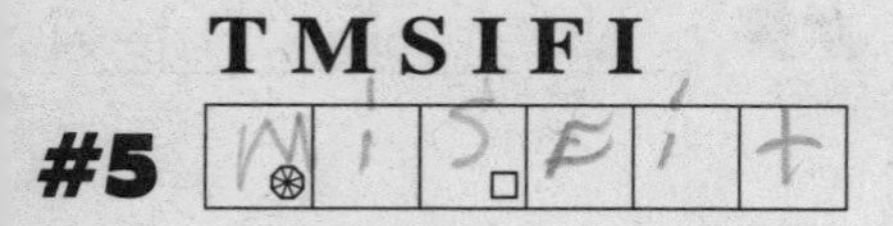

R Y L R B U

#6 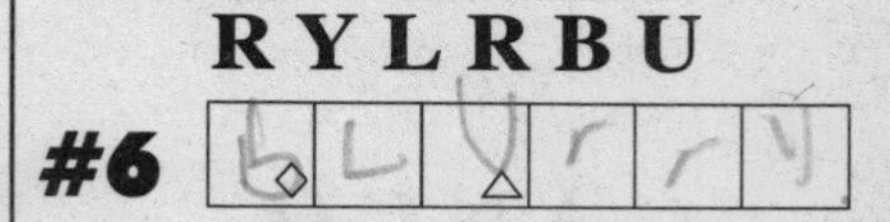

T A T U N M

#7 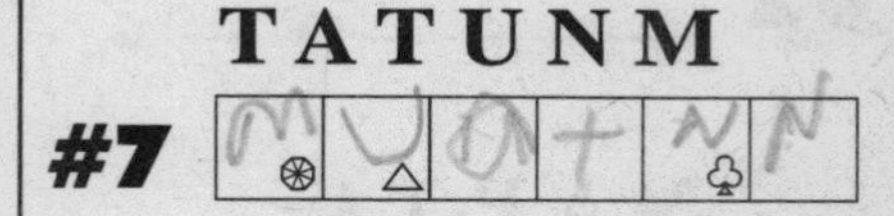

P E U R M J

#8 

A S L O T P

#9 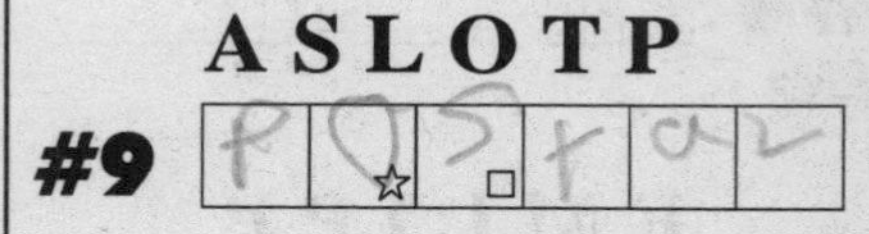

PAT SAJAK'S

GAMES & Puzzles

FEATURING PAT'S PATENT PENDING

CODE LETTER SCRAMBLES

#1 OAGCR

#2 GANCO

#3 NAPTL

#4 VNARTE

#5 EMLIPP

#6 ECLHNC

#7 PAILCD

#8 AISRIN

#9 TOCEKP

PAT SAJAK'S

GAMES & Puzzles

FEATURING PAT'S PATENT PENDING

CODE LETTER SCRAMBLES

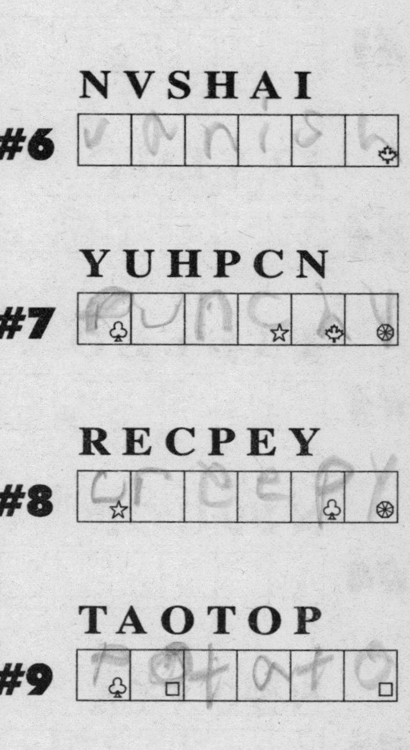

PAT SAJAK'S

GAMES & Puzzles

FEATURING PAT'S PATENT PENDING

CODE LETTER SCRAMBLES

KESNNU

#1

		△	☆		△

ITVIMC

#2

					♡

TAGUEO

#3

			♣		

NIPCCI

#4

			△		

NSGVIA

#5

	♣			△	

TESFYA

#6

	♣				

AECBNO

#7

		♣			△

UMAOTN

#8

♣	♡			△	

HSKRNU

#9

				△	☆

PAT SAJAK'S

GAMES & Puzzles

FEATURING PAT'S PATENT PENDING

CODE LETTER SCRAMBLES

ULAOD

#1

URMLE

#2

RMUBC

#3

UYPMGR

#4

TFUHGO

#5

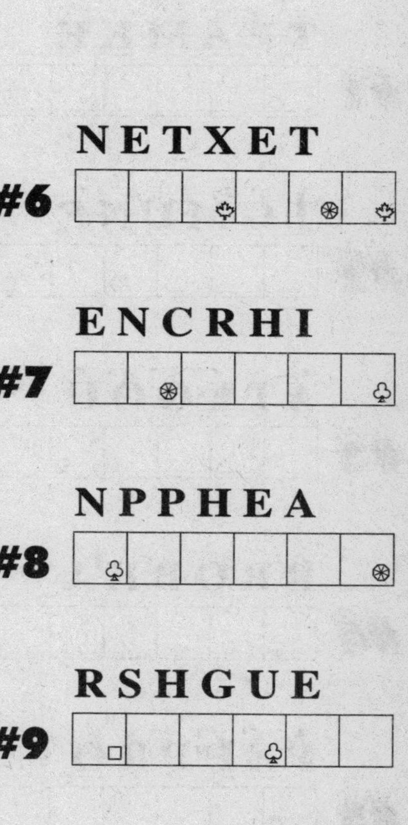

NETXET

#6

ENCRHI

#7

NPPHEA

#8

RSHGUE

#9

PAT SAJAK'S

GAMES & Puzzles

FEATURING PAT'S PATENT PENDING

CODE LETTER SCRAMBLES

TRAMKE

#1 ☐◇ ☐ ☐ ☐ ☐ ☐

TGMUNE

#2 ☐ ☐△ ☐ ☐◇ ☐ ☐□

ATEGOU

#3 ☐ ☐△ ☐ ☐ ☐□ ☐

RROBHA

#4 ☐♣ ☐ ☐ ☐ ☐ ☐

PEHPRO

#5 ☐♣ ☐ ☐ ☐ ☐ ☐

UDNFRE

#6 ☐ ☐ ☐🍁 ☐△ ☐ ☐

EEMLHT

#7 ☐♣ ☐ ☐ ☐◇ ☐ ☐

SUEFRE

#8 ☐ ☐ ☐🍁 ☐△ ☐ ☐

HLBREA

#9 ☐♣ ☐ ☐ ☐ ☐ ☐

PAT SAJAK'S

GAMES & Puzzles

FEATURING PAT'S PATENT PENDING

CODE LETTER SCRAMBLES

GETAEN

#1 ☐ ☐☆ ☐ ☐ ☐ ☐☆

VWLSIE

#2 ☐ ☐ ☐ ☐◇ ☐☆ ☐

RBRBEA

#3 ☐ ☐ ☐ ☐ ☐☆ ☐

NEOJID

#4 ☐ ☐ ☐ ☐ ☐☆ ☐⊛

RVEONG

#5 ☐ ☐ ☐◇ ☐☆ ☐ ☐

EIETPT

#6 ☐○ ☐☆ ☐ ☐ ☐ ☐☆

SUTDNI

#7 ☐ ☐ ☐⊛ ☐ ☐ ☐

GEPTIL

#8 ☐○ ☐ ☐ ☐ ☐☆ ☐

RPNOES

#9 ☐○ ☐☆ ☐ ☐ ☐ ☐

PAT SAJAK'S

GAMES & Puzzles

FEATURING PAT'S PATENT PENDING

CODE LETTER SCRAMBLES

EPRPUL

#1 ☐ ♧ ☐ △ ♧ □ ◇

BIPOAH

#2 ♧ ☆

DORINO

#3 ⊛ ☆ ☆ △

ETDECI

#4 ◇ ◇

MBTUEL

#5 □ ◇

RTATNY

#6 △ ⊛

LWAPLO

#7 □ □ ☆ ♧

TEDFAE

#8 ◇ ◇

BVRLAE

#9 ◇ △ □

PAT SAJAK'S

GAMES & Puzzles

FEATURING PAT'S PATENT PENDING

CODE LETTER SCRAMBLES

BANDPE

#1

SESSAS

#2

TADYIN

#3

YIFRUT

#4

FIFMUN

#5

PAT SAJAK'S

GAMES & Puzzles

FEATURING PAT'S PATENT PENDING

CODE LETTER SCRAMBLES

ELRCYE

#1 | | ◇ | | | | ♧ | ☆ |

OCULKN

#2 | | | | | ◇ | △ |

GHRONT

#3 | ♡ | ○ | ♧ | | | |

AMUDIR

#4 | ♧ | | | | | |

TTALET

#5 | ♡ | | ♡ | ♡ | | |

RYHERS

#6 | | ○ | | ♧ | ♧ | ☆ |

CELOOT

#7 | | ◇ | | | | ♡ |

TWKICE

#8 | | | ◇ | △ | | ♡ |

HYROTN

#9 | ♡ | ○ | | ♧ | | ☆ |

PAT SAJAK'S

GAMES & Puzzles

FEATURING PAT'S PATENT PENDING

CODE LETTER SCRAMBLES

TYIMSC

#1

SLIALE

#2

PARCHO

#3

BYOPIS

#4

GACCON

#5

PAT SAJAK'S

GAMES & Puzzles

FEATURING PAT'S PATENT PENDING

CODE LETTER SCRAMBLES

LOBGGE

#1 | | △ | ☆ | ☆ | | |

INGUMP

#2 | | | | ♧ | ☆ | |

GRIFTH

#3 | | ✿ | | ☆ | ◇ | |

GHOUFT

#4 | | △ | ♧ | ☆ | ◇ | |

WARMOR

#5 | | | ✿ | ✿ | △ | |

THKING

#6 | ♡ | | | ☆ | ◇ | |

DAGGEG

#7 | ☆ | | ☆ | ☆ | | |

GROOFE

#8 | | △ | ✿ | | ☆ | △ |

HERACK

#9 | ◇ | | | ♡ | | ✿ |

PAT SAJAK'S

GAMES & Puzzles

FEATURING PAT'S PATENT PENDING

CODE LETTER SCRAMBLES

#1 DRABER

#2 CYLEER

#3 TANKEL

#4 KEIBOO

#5 GRAYCG

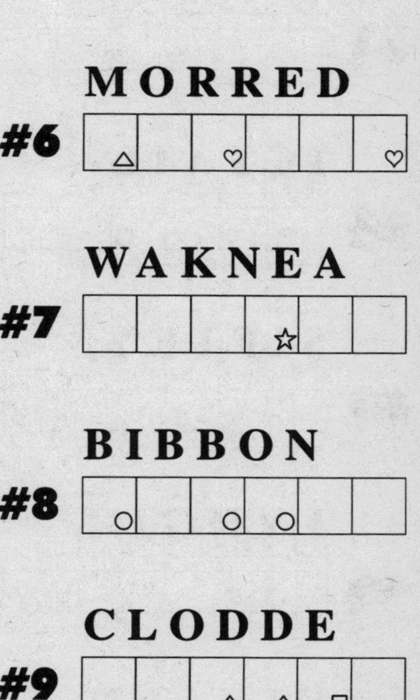

PAT SAJAK'S

GAMES & Puzzles

FEATURING PAT'S PATENT PENDING

CODE LETTER SCRAMBLES

#1 DETODT

#2 ICTAIL

#3 SIFTEY

#4 LYHGIH

#5 DINALN

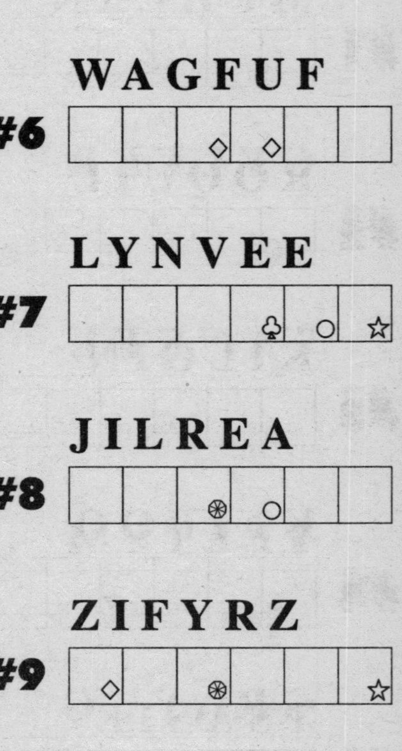

PAT SAJAK'S

GAMES & Puzzles

FEATURING PAT'S PATENT PENDING

CODE LETTER SCRAMBLES

MUHEAN

#1

ROQUIL

#2

KILGIN

#3

TELTEM

#4

TSASIE

#5

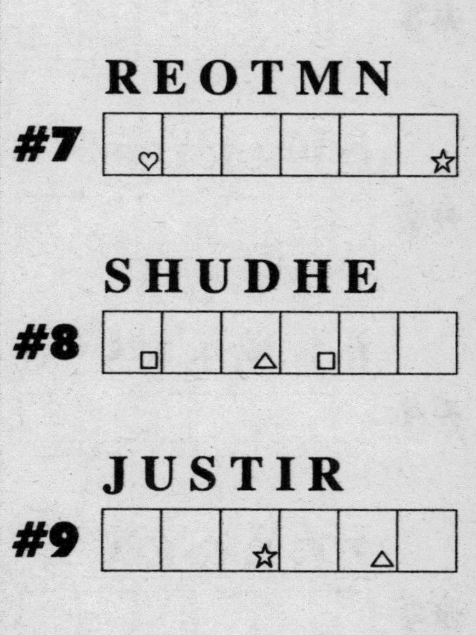

PAT SAJAK'S

GAMES & Puzzles

FEATURING PAT'S PATENT PENDING

CODE LETTER SCRAMBLES

MENTGU

#1 □ □♣ □ □ □ □☆

AONECT

#2 □ □♡ □ □ □ □

LPREUP

#3 □ □♣ □ □ □◇ □

RUMEES

#4 □ □ □ □♣ □ □

ZGBOEA

#5 □☆ □ □ □ □ □

GRITFH

#6 □ □ □ □☆ □△ □

TFUHOR

#7 □ □ □♣ □ □ □△

CURHNC

#8 □♡ □ □♣ □ □♡ □△

LDPYEO

#9 □ □ □ □◇ □ □

PAT SAJAK'S

GAMES & Puzzles

FEATURING PAT'S PATENT PENDING

CODE LETTER SCRAMBLES

ADUELL

#1 ☐ ☐△ ☐△ ☐ ☐ ☐

CRABKE

#2 ☐ ☐ ☐♡ ☐◇ ☐ ☐

PANTAC

#3 ☐♡ ☐ ☐ ☐ ☐ ☐♣

CLAKCE

#4 ☐♡ ☐ ☐♡ ☐◇ ☐△ ☐

CHINFL

#5 ☐ ☐△ ☐ ☐ ☐♡ ☐

UTRIPY

#6 ☐♣ ☐ ☐ ☐ ☐ ☐□

GRINCY

#7 ☐♡ ☐ ☐□ ☐ ☐ ☐☆

VARGLE

#8 ☐☆ ☐ ☐ ☐ ☐ ☐△

LIELOC

#9 ☐♡ ☐ ☐△ ☐△ ☐ ☐

PAT SAJAK'S

GAMES & Puzzles

FEATURING PAT'S PATENT PENDING

CODE LETTER SCRAMBLES

SHIVAR

#1

CLYKUP

#2

TRHOWN

#3

FINCET

#4

VINGGI

#5

PLOYJA

#6

GIRRED

#7

OWNNER

#8

SOCCAT

#9

PAT SAJAK'S

GAMES & Puzzles

FEATURING PAT'S PATENT PENDING

CODE LETTER SCRAMBLES

PTUPEP

#1

	♧				□

CLIPES

#2

☆			△		

DORUSH

#3

☆				♧	

DATTEM

#4

⊛	❦	□	□		

TROVEL

#5

					□

SLOMAN

#6

☆	❦		⊛		◇

HAPNOR

#7

				❦	◇

ROMMIE

#8

⊛		⊛		△	

EMBRIL

#9

	△	⊛			

PAT SAJAK'S

GAMES & Puzzles

FEATURING PAT'S PATENT PENDING

CODE LETTER SCRAMBLES

#1 D A H E R C

♡					☆

#2 W I E H T N

△			□		

#3 B Y R W N A

♣		♡	△		

#4 O W E N O D

△			☆		

#5 P R M C E A

	♡				

#6 Z B R U Z E

♣					

#7 O P I T T E

□			□		

#8 R E U D A G

♡					☆

#9 T I H R W E

△		□			

PAT SAJAK'S

GAMES & Puzzles

FEATURING PAT'S PATENT PENDING

CODE LETTER SCRAMBLES

#1 CHADTE

#2 OGRUBE

#3 CARFAS

#4 HUCCOR

#5 PEARME

PAT SAJAK'S
GAMES & Puzzles

FEATURING PAT'S PATENT PENDING
CODE LETTER SCRAMBLES

EMTRON
#1 ☐ ◇ ☐ ♧ ☐ ☐ ☐

RSMQUI
#2 ☐ □ ☐ ☐ ☐ ☐ ◇

WRYIEN
#3 ☐ ☐ ♧ ☐ ☐ ☐

MOATUN
#4 ☐ ◇ ☐ ☐ ♧ ☐

NOOSAL
#5 □ ☐ ☐ ☐ ☐ ♧

USPURM
#6 ☐ ☐ ◇ ☐ ☐ □

LETDEM
#7 ◇ ☐ ☐ ☐ ☐ ☆

SABMAL
#8 ☐ ☐ ☐ □ ☐ ◇

CEDUSE
#9 □ ☐ ☆ ☐ ☐ ☐

PAT SAJAK'S

GAMES & Puzzles

FEATURING PAT'S PATENT PENDING

CODE LETTER SCRAMBLES

VERPON

#1 ☆ _ _ _ _ _

EZEHEW

#2 △ _ _ _ _ _

LIMPPE

#3 ☆ _ _ ☆ _ _

EPOUTE

#4 ♣ _ _ ☆ _ _

PSOPAE

#5 _ ☆ ☆ _ _ _

INNPET

#6 ♣ _ _ ☆ _ _

YAAPPA

#7 ☆ _ ☆ _ _ _

CTHREW

#8 △ _ _ ♣ _ _

YANYAW

#9 _ _ _ △ _ _

PAT SAJAK'S

GAMES & Puzzles

FEATURING PAT'S PATENT PENDING

CODE LETTER SCRAMBLES

RHBIYD

#1

	○				□

YALDIV

#2

			□		○

YOSUBB

#3

					○

NOYANE

#4

		○			

AMAGED

#5

□				♣	

YAPADY

#6

		○	□		○

YOPLED

#7

□					○

RAFODF

#8

					□

GANEYC

#9

	♣				○

PAT SAJAK'S

GAMES & Puzzles

\# 

FEATURING PAT'S PATENT PENDING

CODE LETTER SCRAMBLES

#1 A E H N G C

□	♡				

#2 M B O E E C

		□	◇	☆	

#3 D O W N O E

	◇	◇	♧		

#4 D O R A M N

			♧	◇	☆

#5 N L E Y O L

	◇				△

#6 B S A Y B H

	♡				△

#7 A Y N C K R

□					△

#8 R O A U D N

		◇			♧

#9 H B C U Y B

□	♡				△

PAT SAJAK'S

GAMES & Puzzles

FEATURING PAT'S PATENT PENDING

CODE LETTER SCRAMBLES

GTNEHL

#1 ☐ ☐ ☐♡ ☐□ ☐ ☐☆

UMNRBE

#2 ☐♡ ☐ ☐△ ☐◇ ☐ ☐

RLSOLC

#3 ☐ ☐♣ ☐ ☐ ☐ ☐

ULHMBE

#4 ☐☆ ☐ ☐△ ☐◇ ☐ ☐

AHOSWD

#5 ☐ ☐☆ ☐ ☐ ☐ ☐

AGLONO

#6 ☐ ☐ ☐□ ☐ ☐ ☐♡

MHIETR

#7 ☐☆ ☐ ☐ ☐△ ☐ ☐

GLYCAE

#8 ☐ ☐ ☐□ ☐ ☐♣ ☐

CNIEVO

#9 ☐♡ ☐ ☐ ☐ ☐♣ ☐

PAT SAJAK'S

GAMES & Puzzles

FEATURING PAT'S PATENT PENDING

CODE LETTER SCRAMBLES

ELWEYK

#1 ☐ ☐♣ ☐♣ ☐☆ ☐ ☐△

TRSSES

#2 ☐ ☐ ☐ ☐♣ ☐ ☐

DLUYOL

#3 ☐ ☐ ☐ ☐ ☐ ☐△

EKLCRO

#4 ☐ ☐ ☐ ☐☆ ☐♣ ☐

TEPYTR

#5 ☐ ☐ ☐♣ ☐ ☐ ☐△

ECYPHA

#6 ☐ ☐♣ ☐ ☐ ☐ ☐△

LEALYG

#7 ☐ ☐ ☐ ☐ ☐♣ ☐△

TNIEMT

#8 ☐ ☐ ☐ ☐ ☐♣ ☐

YMIFLA

#9 ☐ ☐ ☐ ☐ ☐ ☐△

PAT SAJAK'S

GAMES & Puzzles

FEATURING PAT'S PATENT PENDING

CODE LETTER SCRAMBLES

RARBLE

#1

MRPETI

#2

FIOTTU

#3

RCHHUC

#4

ECVRLE

#5

TRLETE

#6

ARFLMO

#7

CLDOEK

#8

LROELR

#9

PAT SAJAK'S

GAMES & Puzzles

FEATURING PAT'S PATENT PENDING

CODE LETTER SCRAMBLES

#1 TARLUB

♣		△			☆

#2 TRUGET

□	△				

#3 GEEALB

♣			□	☆	

#4 NOSELS

☆					

#5 TIBNAD

♣					

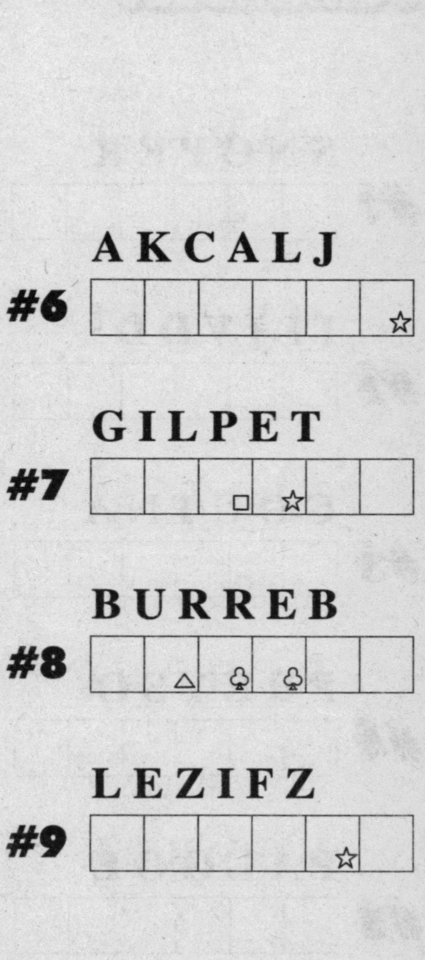

#6 AKCALJ

					☆

#7 GILPET

		□	☆		

#8 BURREB

	△	♣	♣		

#9 LEZIFZ

				☆	

PAT SAJAK'S

GAMES & Puzzles

FEATURING PAT'S PATENT PENDING

CODE LETTER SCRAMBLES

SNOPER

#1

IEIVDD

#2

COUTNA

#3

PREYSO

#4

PALGOL

#5

REPPPE

#6

TYCOOE

#7

SSSERT

#8

HOSECO

#9

PAT SAJAK'S

GAMES & Puzzles

FEATURING PAT'S PATENT PENDING

CODE LETTER SCRAMBLES

#1 YERTAT

#2 GINILV

#3 CHENWR

#4 HOEDMT

#5 ADBETE

#6 VRAEBE

#7 RHYETO

#8 NIVERD

#9 HISDLE

PAT SAJAK'S

GAMES & Puzzles

FEATURING PAT'S PATENT PENDING

CODE LETTER SCRAMBLES

PARBUT

#1

LOAFRM

#2

CATROF

#3

SEALWE

#4

DRAILZ

#5

LOOPAL

#6

SURLAW

#7

HENCAC

#8

SAUTEL

#9

PAT SAJAK'S

GAMES & Puzzles

FEATURING PAT'S PATENT PENDING

CODE LETTER SCRAMBLES

#1 FETEDC

#2 VINEDA

#3 CBBOTA

#4 YOMKEN

#5 IFHISN

#6 ARGAEG

#7 CAKEBD

#8 RKYUET

#9 ELBUBB

PAT SAJAK'S

GAMES & Puzzles

FEATURING PAT'S PATENT PENDING

CODE LETTER SCRAMBLES

HEALGG

#1

PUTSID

#2

TINEIF

#3

BITBAR

#4

ACETKJ

#5

COVENX

#6

LATEBL

#7

HEMCES

#8

LATUAC

#9

PAT SAJAK'S

GAMES & Puzzles

FEATURING PAT'S PATENT PENDING

CODE LETTER SCRAMBLES

RISKHN

#1 ☐ ☐♣ ☐ ☐△ ☐ ☐♡

WOOLHL

#2 ☐♣ ☐○ ☐ ☐ ☐○ ☐

BAVEEH

#3 ☐□ ☐ ☐♣ ☐ ☐ ☐

FLABFE

#4 ☐□ ☐ ☐ ☐ ☐ ☐

ETELKT

#5 ☐♡ ☐ ☐ ☐ ☐ ☐

ZLOZEN

#6 ☐ ☐○ ☐ ☐ ☐ ☐

GAMINK

#7 ☐ ☐ ☐♡ ☐△ ☐ ☐

THIRFG

#8 ☐ ☐ ☐△ ☐ ☐♣ ☐

GTHNIK

#9 ☐♡ ☐ ☐△ ☐ ☐♣ ☐

PAT SAJAK'S

GAMES & Puzzles

FEATURING PAT'S PATENT PENDING

CODE LETTER SCRAMBLES

EEZREF

#1 | △ | | | | |

FLARET

#2 | △ | ♧ | | ☆ | |

GUMSED

#3 | | ◇ | | ○ | |

GLEPED

#4 | ♡ | | | ○ | |

TOREMH

#5 | ◇ | | ☆ | | |

PANNIK

#6 | | ♧ | ♡ | | |

LOLMEW

#7 | ◇ | | | | |

MBCATO

#8 | | | ◇ | | ♧ | ☆

ANONNC

#9 | | ♧ | | | |

PAT SAJAK'S

GAMES & Puzzles

FEATURING PAT'S PATENT PENDING

CODE LETTER SCRAMBLES

SOOUYJ

#1 [ ][ ][ ]□[ ][ ][ ]

CHAING

#2 [ ][ ]☆[ ]◇[ ][ ]△[ ]

KATCAT

#3 [ ][ ][ ][ ][ ]☆[ ]

MHEARM

#4 [ ]◇[ ][ ][ ][ ]○[ ]

OFMATH

#5 [ ][ ][ ][ ]◇[ ][ ]

CLUEDD

#6 [ ]☆[ ][ ][ ][ ][ ]○

LCOIEP

#7 [ ][ ][ ][ ][ ]☆[ ]○

FISHYT

#8 [ ][ ]◇[ ][ ][ ][ ]□

NOTACI

#9 [ ][ ]☆[ ][ ][ ][ ]△

PAT SAJAK'S

GAMES & Puzzles

FEATURING PAT'S PATENT PENDING

CODE LETTER SCRAMBLES

UYDOLC

#1 ☐☆ ☐ ☐ ☐○ ☐ ☐

MUSNOM

#2 ☐ ☐○ ☐ ☐ ☐ ☐

CAMPTI

#3 ☐△ ☐ ☐◇ ☐ ☐☆ ☐♧

MDIEPE

#4 ☐△ ☐ ☐◇ ☐ ☐ ☐

WUDNIN

#5 ☐○ ☐ ☐ ☐△ ☐ ☐

NCETRH

#6 ☐♧ ☐ ☐ ☐ ☐☆ ☐

RUMSTE

#7 ☐ ☐○ ☐ ☐♧ ☐ ☐

PHULIL

#8 ☐○ ☐◇ ☐ ☐△ ☐ ☐

NORHAP

#9 ☐ ☐ ☐◇ ☐ ☐ ☐

PAT SAJAK'S

GAMES & Puzzles

FEATURING PAT'S PATENT PENDING

CODE LETTER SCRAMBLES

FATEED

#1

EONYAN

#2

CAPETC

#3

VIETIN

#4

JETCOB

#5

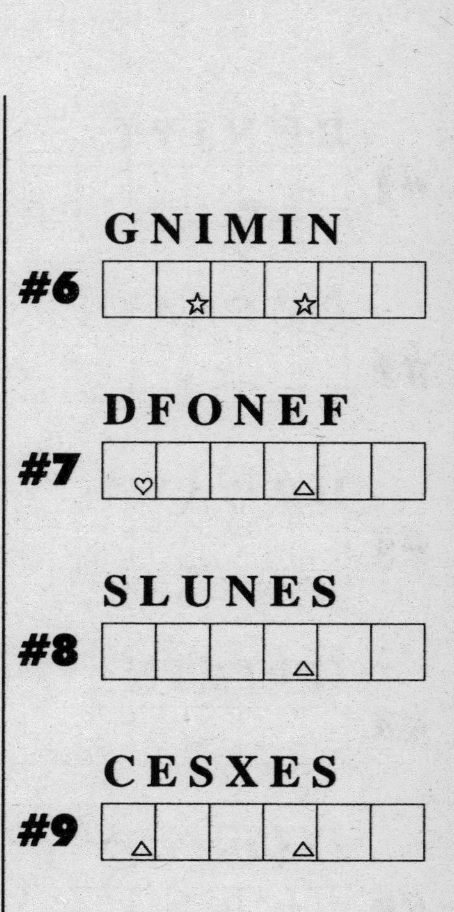

PAT SAJAK'S

GAMES & Puzzles

FEATURING PAT'S PATENT PENDING

CODE LETTER SCRAMBLES

RUNJYI

#1 | | ♡ | | | | □ |

CUESAC

#2 | | | | | ○ | |

DROAWN

#3 | | ♡ | ♣ | | | |

GTIEIN

#4 | | | ♡ | | ☆ | |

UACTSC

#5 | | | | ☆ | | ○ |

EENUNV

#6 | | ♡ | | | | ♡ |

WSLAYA

#7 | | | ♣ | | □ | ○ |

NEATOC

#8 | | | ☆ | | ♡ | |

GLOBON

#9 | | | | | ♡ | |

PAT SAJAK'S

GAMES & Puzzles

FEATURING PAT'S PATENT PENDING

CODE LETTER SCRAMBLES

SUMSSI

#1

PEARME

#2

JOYPAL

#3

ROAMWR

#4

CREAMP

#5

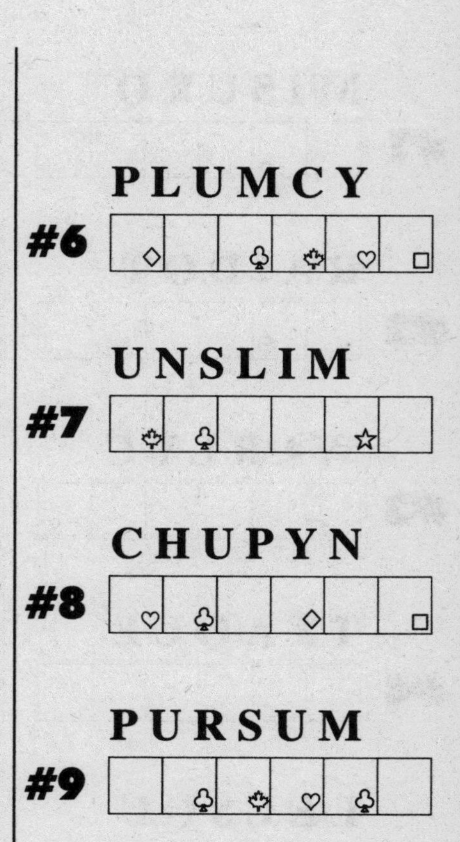

PAT SAJAK'S

GAMES & Puzzles

FEATURING PAT'S PATENT PENDING

CODE LETTER SCRAMBLES

MISURQ

#1 ♧ △ ◇

RAIDOT

#2 ⊛ ◇

WARLYC

#3 □ ♡

TEAQUE

#4 △

LEESQU

#5 ♧ △

IBIDTT

#6 ◇ ⊛ ☆ ◇

QUIBSE

#7 ☆ ◇ ♧ △

TANSCY

#8 ♧ □ ♡

CUTBAD

#9 ☆ ⊛ □

PAT SAJAK'S

GAMES & Puzzles

FEATURING PAT'S PATENT PENDING

CODE LETTER SCRAMBLES

TERMKA

#1 ☐☐☐☐☐☐

TELANK

#2 ☐☐☐☐☐☐

YKLARD

#3 ☐☐☐☐☐☐

ARCHKE

#4 ☐☐☐☐☐☐

RSAVEE

#5 ☐☐☐☐☐☐

LIKERL

#6 ☐☐☐☐☐☐

RAKEUE

#7 ☐☐☐☐☐☐

CRIBEK

#8 ☐☐☐☐☐☐

RUSKNH

#9 ☐☐☐☐☐☐

PAT SAJAK'S

GAMES & Puzzles

FEATURING PAT'S PATENT PENDING

CODE LETTER SCRAMBLES

PLOTEP

#1 [ ][□][ ][ ][☆][ ]

ARTYRO

#2 [ ][ ][□][ ][ ][⊛]

HAILTW

#3 [ ][♧][□][ ][ ][☆]

GRONTH

#4 [□][ ][ ][ ][ ][ ]

SFYEAT

#5 [ ][ ][ ][ ][□][⊛]

MISTYE

#6 [ ][□][⊛][ ][♧][ ]

LOUTDN

#7 [ ][ ][□][ ][☆][ ]

SAXYNT

#8 [ ][⊛][ ][□][ ][ ]

REWNYI

#9 [ ][♧][ ][ ][ ][⊛]

PAT SAJAK'S

GAMES & Puzzles

FEATURING PAT'S PATENT PENDING

CODE LETTER SCRAMBLES

SAGEDO

#1 ☐△ ☐ ☐ ☐ ☐(maple leaf) ☐

RAGELY

#2 ☐ ☐ ☐(maple leaf) ☐☆ ☐□ ☐

ROVEDU

#3 ☐△ ☐ ☐ ☐ ☐ ☐

RAILBT

#4 ☐ ☐ ☐ ☐♧ ☐ ☐□

YINTAD

#5 ☐△ ☐ ☐ ☐ ☐ ☐☆

PBSYIO

#6 ☐♧ ☐ ☐ ☐ ☐ ☐☆

ACERHB

#7 ☐♧ ☐ ☐ ☐ ☐ ☐

LUNGEF

#8 ☐ ☐ ☐(maple leaf) ☐ ☐□ ☐

GRINIW

#9 ☐ ☐ ☐ ☐ ☐ ☐(maple leaf)

PAT SAJAK'S

GAMES & Puzzles

FEATURING PAT'S PATENT PENDING

CODE LETTER SCRAMBLES

FCOINF

#1 | | | | | |

AILCAF

#2 | | | | | |

CABNOE

#3 | | | | | |

FCEETD

#4 | | | | | |

SIFYKR

#5 | | | | | |

HISFYT

#6 | | | | | |

TIESBC

#7 | | | | | |

OKIEOC

#8 | | | | | |

THINCE

#9 | | | | | |

PAT SAJAK'S

GAMES & Puzzles

FEATURING PAT'S PATENT PENDING

CODE LETTER SCRAMBLES

REGRUB

#1 | ♧ | | | ◇ | | |

POLHAO

#2 | | | | ✿ | ☆ | |

DEALSD

#3 | ♡ | | | | ☆ | |

SLOTPA

#4 | ✿ | | ♡ | | | ☆ |

CHINFL

#5 | ⊛ | ☆ | | | | |

FLEARO

#6 | ☆ | | | ⊛ | | |

GINDIT

#7 | | | | | | ◇ |

MOBPAL

#8 | | ✿ | ☆ | | | ♧ |

DUELSG

#9 | ♡ | ☆ | | | ◇ | |

PAT SAJAK'S

GAMES & Puzzles

FEATURING PAT'S PATENT PENDING

CODE LETTER SCRAMBLES

LUANAN

#1 ☐☐☐☐☐⊛

CENFED

#2 ♡☐☐◇☐☐

CHABLN

#3 ♧⊛☐☐◇☐

PROACH

#4 ◇☐☐☐☆○

PCYLUM

#5 ◇⊛☐☐○☐

FLEDTY

#6 ☐☐♡☐⊛☐

ROBELO

#7 ♧☆⊛☐☐☆

FEMALA

#8 ☐♡⊛☐☐☐

PEARMC

#9 ◇☐☐○☐☐

PAT SAJAK'S

GAMES & Puzzles

FEATURING PAT'S PATENT PENDING

CODE LETTER SCRAMBLES

CARESE

#1 ☐ ☐(☆) ☐ ☐ ☐(⊛) ☐ ☐

COBYUN

#2 ☐ ☐ ☐ ☐(△) ☐(☆) ☐(♧)

NERUSE

#3 ☐ ☐(△) ☐ ☐ ☐ ☐

YARDFT

#4 ☐(◇) ☐ ☐(⊛) ☐ ☐ ☐(♧)

LGEAGH

#5 ☐ ☐(⊛) ☐(♡) ☐(♡) ☐ ☐

CHARDE

#6 ☐(⊛) ☐ ☐(☆) ☐ ☐ ☐(◇)

RYEINW

#7 ☐ ☐ ☐(△) ☐ ☐ ☐(♧)

CARTOV

#8 ☐(☆) ☐(⊛) ☐ ☐ ☐ ☐

YARING

#9 ☐(♡) ☐ ☐(⊛) ☐ ☐(△) ☐(♧)

PAT SAJAK'S

GAMES & Puzzles

FEATURING PAT'S PATENT PENDING

CODE LETTER SCRAMBLES

#1 REALIJ

#2 SEUEDC

#3 GAMIEP

#4 SEEPOD

#5 CXLIMA

#6 CREAPN

#7 NALDIN

#8 BUADTC

#9 SENTEL

PAT SAJAK'S

GAMES & Puzzles

FEATURING PAT'S PATENT PENDING

CODE LETTER SCRAMBLES

TIDESV

#1

RUBECH

#2

GOLUSH

#3

STUNDI

#4

BLAREH

#5

MADRUI

#6

PACTEU

#7

VEERDI

#8

DOKWRE

#9

PAT SAJAK'S

GAMES & Puzzles

FEATURING PAT'S PATENT PENDING

CODE LETTER SCRAMBLES

RCHDAE

#1 [♣][ ][ ][ ][ ][☆]

TURFIY

#2 [ ][ ][🍁][ ][ ][△]

SQUIBE

#3 [○][ ][♡][ ][🍁][ ]

DREAMK

#4 [ ][♣][ ][ ][ ][☆]

SCULLA

#5 [ ][♣][ ][ ][🍁][♡]

BOPALM

#6 [♣][ ][ ][◇][ ][○]

YANKSE

#7 [♡][ ][ ][♣][ ][△]

CHALKE

#8 [ ][♣][ ][ ][ ][ ]

KSIMEO

#9 [ ][♡][ ][ ][ ][◇]

PAT SAJAK'S

GAMES & Puzzles

FEATURING PAT'S PATENT PENDING

CODE LETTER SCRAMBLES

ERROCG

#1 | | | | | |

AFGULR

#2 | | | | | |

BLRIEM

#3 | | | | | |

DLBIER

#4 | | | | | |

CEMBOE

#5 | | | | | |

NEELKN

#6 | | | | | |

DRCEUS

#7 | | | | | |

TEDILA

#8 | | | | | |

RNOIMF

#9 | | | | | |

PAT SAJAK'S

GAMES & Puzzles

FEATURING PAT'S PATENT PENDING

CODE LETTER SCRAMBLES

EGRME

#1 ☐☐☐☐△☐

LILYH

#2 ☐♣☐✲☐☐☐

OGVRE

#3 ☐△☐☐☐✤☐

EHXAEL

#4 ☐☐☐♣☐☐☐

HGARAN

#5 ☐♣☐☐☐△☐☐

VEAGLR

#6 ☐△☐☐☐✤☐☐

VILAUS

#7 ☐✤☐✲☐☐☐☐

UTOHRF

#8 ☐☐☐☐☐☐♣

ZEOABG

#9 ☐△☐☐☐☐☐

PAT SAJAK'S

GAMES & Puzzles

FEATURING PAT'S PATENT PENDING

CODE LETTER SCRAMBLES

LAAHP

#1 | | | | ○ |

RHDOA

#2 ○ | ⊛ | | | |

ACOLL

#3 | ⊛ | ♧ | | |

HGWITE

#4 ◇ | ☆ | | | ○ |

LEFKCI

#5 | | ♧ | | | ☆

GESVAA

#6 | | | | | ☆

WRINIG

#7 ◇ | | | | |

CNHREW

#8 ◇ | | ☆ | | ♧ | ○

AWAYIR

#9 | | | ◇ | |

PAT SAJAK'S

GAMES & Puzzles

FEATURING PAT'S PATENT PENDING

CODE LETTER SCRAMBLES

SRUVES

#1

LOHPOA

#2

REGORC

#3

RGEILB

#4

ERWNYI

#5

SWDOYR

#6

UHMENA

#7

ETHNDU

#8

BERAMK

#9

PAT SAJAK'S

GAMES & Puzzles

FEATURING PAT'S PATENT PENDING

CODE LETTER SCRAMBLES

MEFLYS

#1 [ ][♡][□][ ][△][♣]

LEPTLE

#2 [ ][ ][△][△][ ][ ]

LRYEAR

#3 [ ][◇][ ][ ][△][♡]

HOUNKO

#4 [☆][ ][○][ ][ ][ ]

RCUVYS

#5 [□][ ][☆][ ][ ][♡]

NOFRUF

#6 [ ][☆][ ][ ][♣][♣]

ARLOME

#7 [ ][ ][ ][◇][△][ ]

LOHUGS

#8 [□][△][ ][☆][ ][○]

FUNIPF

#9 [ ][☆][♣][♣][ ][ ]

PAT SAJAK'S

GAMES & Puzzles

FEATURING PAT'S PATENT PENDING

CODE LETTER SCRAMBLES

#1 BYMLSO

#2 OWTRNH

#3 DEIMEP

#4 LEFEYR

#5 TOCONT

#6 TXFIEA

#7 NUHAEM

#8 LODPYE

#9 BCAYRB

PAT SAJAK'S

GAMES & Puzzles

FEATURING PAT'S PATENT PENDING

CODE LETTER SCRAMBLES

VTELEW

#1 ☐ ♡ ☐ ☐ ☐ △ ☐ □ ☐

OJURIN

#2 ☐ ☐ ♣ ☐ ☐ ◇ ☐

CIARCT

#3 ☐ ☐ ☐ ☐ ♡ ☐ ◇ ☐

RICGYN

#4 ☐ ☐ ☐ ☐ ◇ ☐ ☐

KESIOM

#5 ☐ ☐ ☐ ☐ ◇ ☐ ☆ ☐

CETKOL

#6 ☐ △ ☐ ☐ ☐ ☐ ☐ ♡

AMYEMH

#7 ☐ ☆ ☐ ☐ ☐ ☐ ☐ ☆

VREETR

#8 ☐ ☐ ☐ □ ☐ ☐ ☐ ♡

NRUYUL

#9 ☐ ♣ ☐ ☐ ☐ ♣ ☐ △ ☐

PAT SAJAK'S

GAMES & Puzzles

FEATURING PAT'S PATENT PENDING

CODE LETTER SCRAMBLES

HESLAV

#1 | ☐ ☐♣ ☐ ☐□ ☐☆ ☐ ☐

ESILVW

#2 | ☐ ☐ ☐△ ☐☆ ☐ ☐□

JEERST

#3 | ☐ ☐ ☐ ☐⊛ ☐ ☐

GHAUNT

#4 | ☐ ☐ ☐ ☐ ☐♣ ☐⊛

DECLOK

#5 | ☐□ ☐ ☐ ☐○ ☐ ☐

SHOBIK

#6 | ☐○ ☐△ ☐♡ ☐ ☐ ☐♣

BASORI

#7 | ☐△ ☐ ☐ ☐♡ ☐ ☐

MOITAC

#8 | ☐ ☐⊛ ☐ ☐◇ ☐△ ☐

KLYEEM

#9 | ☐◇ ☐ ☐ ☐○ ☐□ ☐

PAT SAJAK'S

GAMES & Puzzles

FEATURING PAT'S PATENT PENDING

CODE LETTER SCRAMBLES

#1 CHABER

#2 PLAGOL

#3 FLURAG

#4 NERZAB

#5 WAFELD

#6 ZEEFER

#7 SHRUGE

#8 THRIBG

#9 LAUCAS

PAT SAJAK'S

GAMES & Puzzles

FEATURING PAT'S PATENT PENDING

CODE LETTER SCRAMBLES

KESNNU

#1 □ □ □△ □☆ □ □△

ITVIMC

#2 □ □ □ □ □ □♡

TAGUEO

#3 □ □ □ □♣ □ □

NIPCCI

#4 □ □ □ □△ □ □

NSGVIA

#5 □ □♣ □ □ □△ □

TESFYA

#6 □ □♣ □ □ □ □

AECBNO

#7 □ □ □♣ □ □ □△

UMAOTN

#8 □♣ □♡ □ □ □△ □

HSKRNU

#9 □ □ □ □ □△ □☆

PAT SAJAK'S

GAMES & Puzzles

FEATURING PAT'S PATENT PENDING

CODE LETTER SCRAMBLES

SIEVTN

#1 | | △ | | | | ◇ |

CONVEI

#2 | △ | | | | | |

COETBJ

#3 | | ☆ | | | | ◇ |

NXBIGO

#4 | ☆ | | | | △ | |

NAULNA

#5 | | △ | △ | | | |

CNBOOR

#6 | ☆ | | | △ | | |

CIEBRK

#7 | ☆ | | | | | |

PRTYOH

#8 | ◇ | | | | | |

VNIEIT

#9 | | △ | | | ◇ | |

PAT SAJAK'S

GAMES & Puzzles

FEATURING PAT'S PATENT PENDING

CODE LETTER SCRAMBLES

#1 OLGLNA

#2 UPIRTR

#3 AITNNF

#4 CRMTIE

#5 OGLNBO

#6 CSOREC

#7 SBELHU

#8 NROERC

#9 ABTOYN

PAT SAJAK'S

GAMES & Puzzles

FEATURING PAT'S PATENT PENDING

CODE LETTER SCRAMBLES

SORCEA

#1

GEARTT

#2

KORNEB

#3

TTEELR

#4

LICELO

#5

TUNMAU

#6

BEARRL

#7

TOKEPC

#8

RTETBE

#9

PAT SAJAK'S

GAMES & Puzzles

FEATURING PAT'S PATENT PENDING

CODE LETTER SCRAMBLES

GSSINA

#1 ♧ _ _ _ _ △

TUBESO

#2 _ _ ◇ ♡ _ _

LOMNUC

#3 _ _ _ ♡ ☆ △

XTRAIM

#4 ☆ ♧ ◇ _ _ _

TNITEK

#5 _ _ ◇ ◇ _ △

PISMHR

#6 _ _ _ _ ☆ _

GLGJEU

#7 _ ♡ _ _ _ _

IDOSUT

#8 _ ◇ ♡ _ _ _

ELATRE

#9 _ _ _ ♧ ◇ _

PAT SAJAK'S

GAMES & Puzzles

FEATURING PAT'S PATENT PENDING

CODE LETTER SCRAMBLES

KLCUEB

#1

△	♣	☆			

TRUEBT

#2

△	♣				♡

HNTRCE

#3

	♡			☆	

URDRDE

#4

♡	♣				♡

TEETRB

#5

△					♡

ETHRET

#6

					♡

RIAWDZ

#7

	◇			♡	

SUREPU

#8

	♣	♡		♣	

MICOAT

#9

				◇	☆

PAT SAJAK'S

GAMES & Puzzles

FEATURING PAT'S PATENT PENDING

CODE LETTER SCRAMBLES

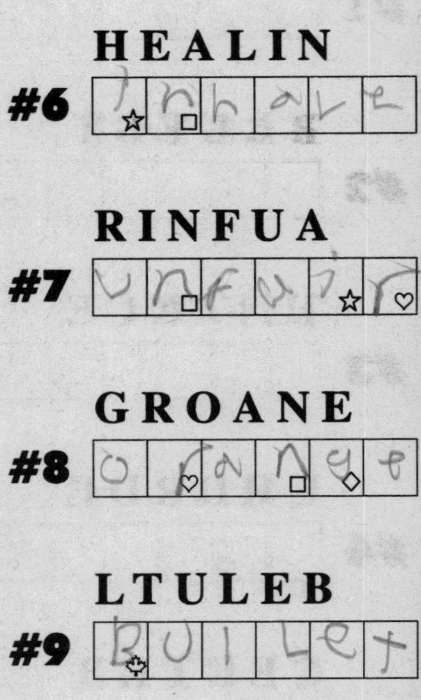

PAT SAJAK'S

GAMES & Puzzles

FEATURING PAT'S PATENT PENDING

CODE LETTER SCRAMBLES

TRIGTY

#1

BABYLF

#2

TIEING

#3

EMOLYH

#4

GFNAHA

#5

UQORIL

GEARUR

SLYRIG

NRAGHA

PAT SAJAK'S

GAMES & Puzzles

FEATURING PAT'S PATENT PENDING

CODE LETTER SCRAMBLES

BDLAKE

#1 | ☆ | | △ | | | ◇ |

BEEMML

#2 | | ○ | ☆ | △ | | ○ |

DROHIR

#3 | ♧ | | | | | ◇ |

BRUUNA

#4 | | | ☆ | | | |

MEEDAN

#5 | ◇ | | ○ | | | |

EMXUEH

#6 | | | ♧ | | ○ | |

BAAMSL

#7 | ☆ | | △ | | | ○ |

SHAMBU

#8 | | ○ | ☆ | | | ♧ |

BLUMHE

#9 | ♧ | | ○ | ☆ | △ | |

PAT SAJAK'S

GAMES & Puzzles

FEATURING PAT'S PATENT PENDING

CODE LETTER SCRAMBLES

CIMOAT

#1

DEERBN

#2

REALMO

#3

ROAMCL

#4

DRYBOW

#5

DAMESK

#6

SHAMBU

#7

LIBRED

#8

NAKEWA

#9

PAT SAJAK'S

GAMES & Puzzles

FEATURING PAT'S PATENT PENDING

CODE LETTER SCRAMBLES

TEAVIA

#1

GETAOU

#2

ZEWEEH

#3

LEWEVT

#4

VAINGH

#5

DICLAP

#6

CIITMV

#7

VORENP

#8

PEIPRZ

#9

PAT SAJAK'S

GAMES & Puzzles

FEATURING PAT'S PATENT PENDING

CODE LETTER SCRAMBLES

OLTJSE

#1

VIEWSL

#2

SHIPIM

#3

ELSEVH

#4

LOSTIN

#5

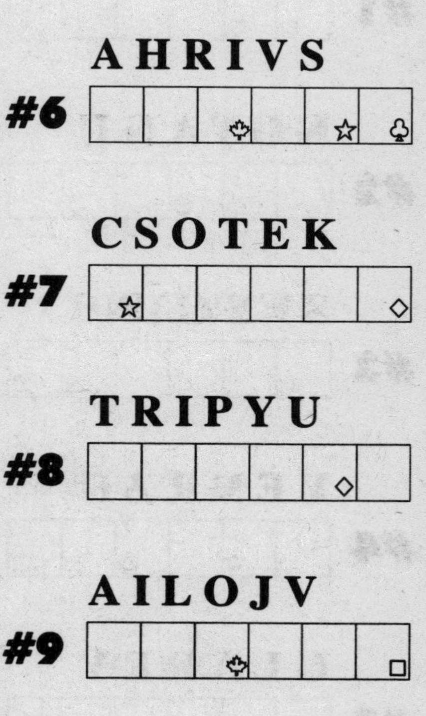

PAT SAJAK'S

GAMES & Puzzles

FEATURING PAT'S PATENT PENDING

CODE LETTER SCRAMBLES

#1 RVIRED

□	♡				♡

#2 NOYANE

	♣	⊛		♣	

#3 SLYGIN

		♣		△	⊛

#4 YENRZF

	♡		♣		⊛

#5 GLAREY

	♡		⊛	△	

#6 LAYTEN

♣				△	⊛

#7 BLIRGE

		♡			△

#8 TOCKED

□					

#9 USJOOY

		⊛			

PAT SAJAK'S

GAMES & Puzzles

FEATURING PAT'S PATENT PENDING

CODE LETTER SCRAMBLES

PYGONS

#1

RURAGE

#2

BRIBEG

#3

BERRUG

#4

GUMENT

#5

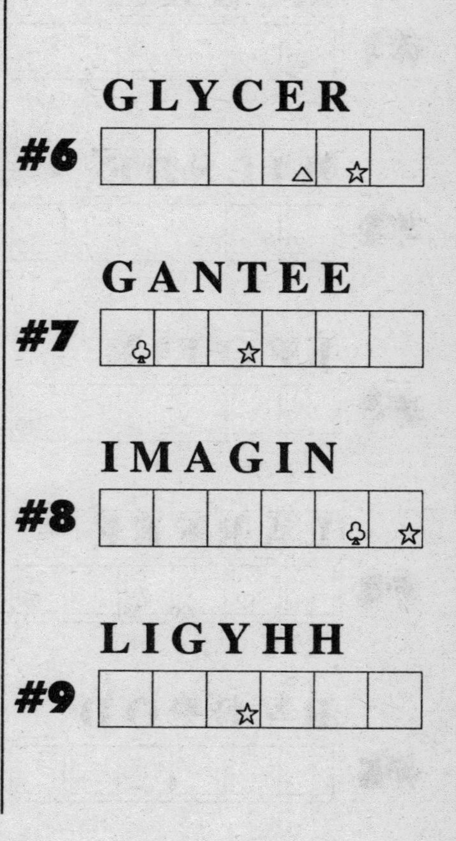

PAT SAJAK'S

GAMES & Puzzles

FEATURING PAT'S PATENT PENDING

CODE LETTER SCRAMBLES

MSRHIP

#1

HILSDE

#2

FPOTIR

#3

LARFEF

#4

RYOPOD

#5

VREETR

#6

VSYROA

#7

SEEFTW

#8

WRODYS

#9

PAT SAJAK'S

GAMES & Puzzles

FEATURING PAT'S PATENT PENDING

CODE LETTER SCRAMBLES

YGOVRO

#1

FETEDC

#2

HNTGIK

#3

OCGURA

#4

HGELNT

#5

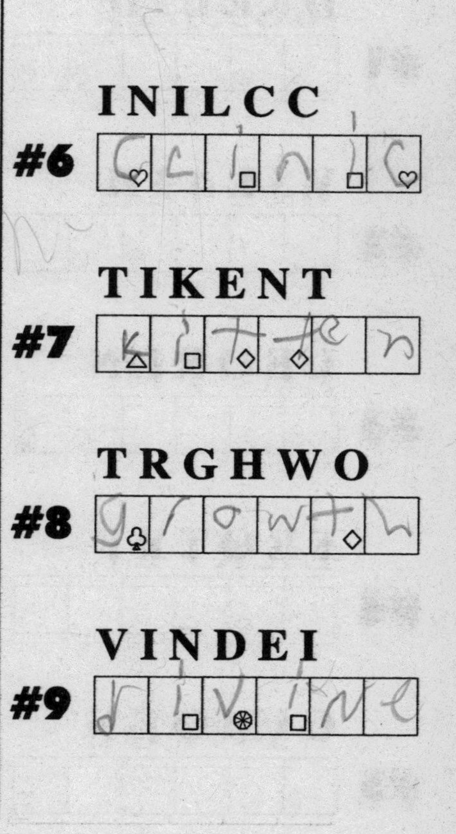

PAT SAJAK'S

GAMES & Puzzles

FEATURING PAT'S PATENT PENDING

CODE LETTER SCRAMBLES

DFELID

#1

VSLAIH

#2

LEORLN

#3

FEOTRF

#4

CIMOEN

#5

SISNIT

#6

CFEIKL

#7

ATGREH

#8

TGLNHE

#9

PAT SAJAK'S

GAMES & Puzzles

FEATURING PAT'S PATENT PENDING

CODE LETTER SCRAMBLES

DPLAED

#1 ☐ ♧☐ △☐ ☐ ☐ ◇☐

TTEOPN

#2 ♧☐ ⊛☐ ☐ ◇☐ □☐ ☐

ELOLWF

#3 ☐ ◇☐ ☐ ☐ ⊛☐ ☐

RILTEP

#4 ☐ ☐ ☐ ♧☐ ☐ ◇☐

BENMRU

#5 □☐ ☐ ☐ ☐ ◇☐ ☐

PNEEWH

#6 □☐ ◇☐ ♧☐ ☐ ◇☐ ☐

AUTEPC

#7 ☐ ◇☐ △☐ ☐ ☐ ♧☐

KPCETA

#8 ♧☐ △☐ ☐ ♡☐ ◇☐ ☐

CTSEHK

#9 ☐ ♡☐ ◇☐ ☐ ☐ ☐

PAT SAJAK'S

GAMES & Puzzles

FEATURING PAT'S PATENT PENDING

CODE LETTER SCRAMBLES

MUVLEO

#1 | ◇ | | | | △ | |

WTRNHO

#2 | | □ | | | ♧ | |

RWTYOH

#3 | ♧ | | | | □ | |

DAIECV

#4 | ⊛ | | ◇ | | ♡ | |

AANULN

#5 | ⊛ | | | | ⊛ | |

RTNATY

#6 | | | | ⊛ | | |

TWNDAE

#7 | ♧ | ⊛ | | | | |

CIEODV

#8 | ◇ | | | ♡ | | |

MRTUAA

#9 | | | ⊛ | | △ | ⊛ |

PAT SAJAK'S

GAMES & Puzzles

FEATURING PAT'S PATENT PENDING

CODE LETTER SCRAMBLES

DABINT

#1 | | ♡ | | | □ | ⊛ |

YAOENN

#2 | ♡ | | ♣ | ◇ | | |

GIMENL

#3 | △ | □ | | | | |

TAOFRM

#4 | | ◇ | | △ | ♡ | ⊛ |

TCAYTH

#5 | | | ♡ | ⊛ | ⊛ | ♣ |

ANOCNN

#6 | | ♡ | | | ◇ | |

GMVNIO

#7 | △ | ◇ | | □ | | |

BLMEFU

#8 | | | △ | | | |

GNAEYC

#9 | ♡ | | | | | ♣ |

PAT SAJAK'S

GAMES & Puzzles

FEATURING PAT'S PATENT PENDING

CODE LETTER SCRAMBLES

#1 RPULEP

	♧				△

#2 AAIFRS

		⊛			

#3 DSEMOT

♡			△		

#4 ERZBYE

		△	△		□

#5 CUBELK

	♧		◇		△

#6 KEOTCR

			◇	△	

#7 SREUEF

	△	⊛	♧		△

#8 LDPEDU

	♧				△

#9 STMYOL

♡					□

PAT SAJAK'S

GAMES & Puzzles

FEATURING PAT'S PATENT PENDING

CODE LETTER SCRAMBLES

RUBYLR

#1

BELEMM

#2

NFOYLD

#3

RTPEYT

#4

LDCUDE

#5

NTCUYO

#6

YOOECT

#7

RSEUEN

#8

TYABON

#9

PAT SAJAK'S

GAMES & Puzzles

FEATURING PAT'S PATENT PENDING

CODE LETTER SCRAMBLES

#1 U N R R E N

#2 S G I P S O

#3 N A P R C E

#4 P G U Y M R

#5 U P C L T S

#6 P A H E N P

#7 R A S L Y A

#8 T V R R E E

#9 C P I A Y R

PAT SAJAK'S

GAMES & Puzzles

FEATURING PAT'S PATENT PENDING

CODE LETTER SCRAMBLES

CGNEAL

#1

FUIMNF

#2

SLIHAV

#3

KNINPA

#4

RTPYAS

#5

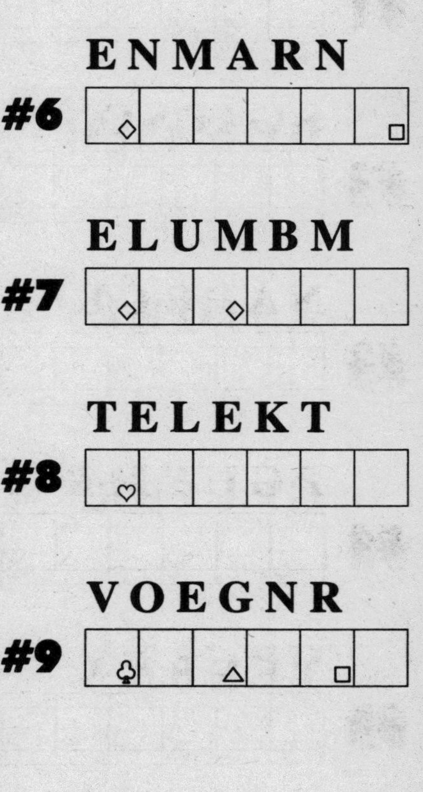

PAT SAJAK'S

GAMES & Puzzles

FEATURING PAT'S PATENT PENDING

CODE LETTER SCRAMBLES

SOPOEP

#1

DOSAWH

#2

ASIORL

#3

CPUIPK

#4

TEEBNA

#5

TURAOH

#6

NOADWR

#7

EKASTB

#8

AECIEP

#9

PAT SAJAK'S

GAMES & Puzzles

FEATURING PAT'S PATENT PENDING

CODE LETTER SCRAMBLES

UNAANL

#1 ☐ ☐ ☐ ♡ ☐ ♣

SOCOEH

#2 ◇ ☐ ☐ ☐ ☐ ☐

ALCNUY

#3 ♣ ♡ ◇ ☐ ☐ △

DIARSU

#4 ☐ ☐ □ ☐ ♡ ☐

SCEOTL

#5 ◇ ♣ ☐ ☐ ☐ ☐

LTIEPR

#6 ☐ ☐ ☐ ☐ ♣ ☐

AODLRL

#7 □ ☐ ♣ ♣ ☐ ☐

RRYLUB

#8 ☐ ♣ ♡ ☐ ☐ △

FAETFC

#9 ☐ ☐ ☐ ☐ ◇ ☐

ANSWERS

HOW DO YOU RANK?

Zero completed = F
One or two completed = D
Three or four completed = C
Five completed = B
Six completed = B+
Seven completed = A-
Eight completed = A
Nine completed = A+

PUZZLE #1
1. UNION
2. YODEL
3. WHOLE
4. HYBRID
5. BOTHER
6. FABRIC
7. UPHILL
8. NESTLE
9. ADVERB

PUZZLE #2
1. PANTS
2. BLUES
3. ABRUPT
4. AMOUNT
5. BRIDLE
6. CAMERA
7. JARGON
8. CHOSEN
9. MANGLE

PUZZLE #3
1. TIDAL
2. VODKA
3. FLUME
4. NATIVE
5. BITTER
6. FLIMSY
7. ACTUAL
8. MASCOT
9. OCTANE

PUZZLE #4
1. KNOWN
2. SCUBA
3. MORON
4. NORMAL
5. MISFIT
6. BLURRY
7. MUTANT
8. JUMPER
9. POSTAL

PUZZLE #5
1. CARGO
2. CONGA
3. PLANT
4. TAVERN
5. PIMPLE
6. CLENCH
7. PLACID
8. RAISIN
9. POCKET

PUZZLE #6
1. PURGE
2. PERKY
3. LATCH
4. COWARD
5. JALOPY
6. VANISH
7. PUNCHY
8. CREEPY
9. POTATO

PUZZLE #7
1. SUNKEN
2. VICTIM
3. OUTAGE
4. PICNIC
5. SAVING
6. SAFETY
7. BEACON
8. AMOUNT
9. SHRUNK

PUZZLE #8
1. ALOUD
2. LEMUR
3. CRUMB
4. GRUMPY
5. FOUGHT
6. EXTENT
7. ENRICH
8. HAPPEN
9. GUSHER

PUZZLE #9
1. MARKET
2. NUTMEG
3. OUTAGE
4. HARBOR
5. HOPPER
6. REFUND
7. HELMET
8. REFUSE
9. HERBAL

PUZZLE #10
1. NEGATE
2. SWIVEL
3. BARBER
4. JOINED
5. GOVERN
6. PETITE
7. NUDIST
8. PIGLET
9. PERSON

PUZZLE #11
1. PURPLE
2. PHOBIA
3. INDOOR
4. DECEIT
5. TUMBLE
6. TYRANT
7. WALLOP
8. DEFEAT
9. VERBAL

PUZZLE #12
1. BEDPAN
2. ASSESS
3. DAINTY
4. FRUITY
5. MUFFIN
6. JOYOUS
7. QUEASY
8. UNWIND
9. SNAZZY

PUZZLE #13
1. CELERY
2. UNLOCK
3. THRONG
4. RADIUM
5. TATTLE
6. SHERRY
7. OCELOT
8. WICKET
9. THORNY

PUZZLE #14
1. MYSTIC
2. ALLIES
3. CARHOP
4. BIOPSY
5. COGNAC
6. APLOMB
7. BUNGLE
8. ENGULF
9. AMOEBA

PUZZLE #15
1. BOGGLE
2. IMPUGN
3. FRIGHT
4. FOUGHT
5. MARROW
6. KNIGHT
7. GAGGED
8. FOREGO
9. HACKER

ANSWERS

PUZZLE #16
1. BARRED
2. CELERY
3. ANKLET
4. BOOKIE
5. CRAGGY
6. DORMER
7. AWAKEN
8. BOBBIN
9. CODDLE

PUZZLE #17
1. DOTTED
2. ITALIC
3. FEISTY
4. HIGHLY
5. INLAND
6. GUFFAW
7. EVENLY
8. JAILER
9. FRIZZY

PUZZLE #18
1. HUMANE
2. LIQUOR
3. LIKING
4. METTLE
5. SIESTA
6. PRANCE
7. MENTOR
8. HUSHED
9. JURIST

PUZZLE #19
1. NUTMEG
2. OCTANE
3. PURPLE
4. RESUME
5. GAZEBO
6. FRIGHT
7. FOURTH
8. CRUNCH
9. DEPLOY

PUZZLE #20
1. ALLUDE
2. BACKER
3. CATNAP
4. CACKLE
5. FLINCH
6. PURITY
7. CRYING
8. GRAVEL
9. COLLIE

PUZZLE #21
1. RAVISH
2. PLUCKY
3. THROWN
4. INFECT
5. GIVING
6 JALOPY
7. GIRDER
8. RENOWN
9. ACCOST

PUZZLE #22
1 PUPPET
2. SPLICE
3. SHROUD
4. MATTED
5. REVOLT
6. SALMON
7. ORPHAN
8. MEMOIR
9. LIMBER

PUZZLE #23
1. ARCHED
2. WHITEN
3. BRAWNY
4. WOODEN
5. CAMPER
6. BUZZER
7. TIPTOE
8. ARGUED
9. WITHER

PUZZLE #24
1. DETACH
2. BROGUE
3. FRACAS
4. CROUCH
5. AMPERE
6. CLERGY
7. AVIATE
8. CINDER
9. DIVEST

PUZZLE #25
1. MENTOR
2. SQUIRM
3. WINERY
4. AMOUNT
5. SALOON
6. RUMPUS
7. MELTED
8. BALSAM
9. SEDUCE

PUZZLE #26
1. PROVEN
2. WHEEZE
3. PIMPLE
4. TOUPEE
5. APPOSE
6. TENPIN
7. PAPAYA
8. WRETCH
9. ANYWAY

PUZZLE #27
1. HYBRID
2. AVIDLY
3. BUSBOY
4. ANYONE
5. DAMAGE
6. PAYDAY
7. DEPLOY
8. AFFORD
9. AGENCY

PUZZLE #28
1. CHANGE
2. BECOME
3. WOODEN
4. RANDOM
5. LONELY
6. SHABBY
7. CRANKY
8 AROUND
9. CHUBBY

PUZZLE #29
1. LENGTH
2. NUMBER
3. SCROLL
4. HUMBLE
5. SHADOW
6. LAGOON
7. HERMIT
8. LEGACY
9.NOVICE

PUZZLE #30
1. WEEKLY
2. STRESS
3. LOUDLY
4. LOCKER
5. PRETTY
6. PEACHY
7. GALLEY
8. MITTEN
9. FAMILY

PUZZLE #31
1. BARREL
2. PERMIT
3. OUTFIT
4. CHURCH
5. CLEVER
6. LETTER
7. FORMAL
8. LOCKED
9. ROLLER

PUZZLE #32
1. BRUTAL
2. GUTTER
3. BEAGLE
4. LESSON
5. BANDIT
6. JACKAL
7. PIGLET
8. RUBBER
9. FIZZLE

PUZZLE #33
1. PERSON
2. DIVIDE
3. TOUCAN
4. OSPREY
5. GALLOP
6. PEPPER
7. COYOTE
8. STRESS
9. CHOOSE

PUZZLE #34
1. TREATY
2. LIVING
3. WRENCH
4. METHOD
5. DEBATE
6. BEAVER
7. THEORY
8. DRIVEN
9. SHIELD

PUZZLE #35
1. ABRUPT
2. FORMAL
3. FACTOR
4. WEASEL
5. LIZARD
6. APOLLO
7. WALRUS
8. CHANCE
9. SALUTE

ANSWERS

PUZZLE #36
1. DEFECT
2. INVADE
3. BOBCAT
4. MONKEY
5. FINISH
6. GARAGE
7. BACKED
8. TURKEY
9. BUBBLE

PUZZLE #37
1. HAGGLE
2. STUPID
3. FINITE
4. RABBIT
5. JACKET
6. CONVEX
7. BALLET
8. SCHEME
9. ACTUAL

PUZZLE #38
1. SHRINK
2. HOLLOW
3. BEHAVE
4. BAFFLE
5. KETTLE
6. NOZZLE
7. MAKING
8. FRIGHT
9. KNIGHT

PUZZLE #39
1. FREEZE
2. FALTER
3. SMUDGE
4. PLEDGE
5. MOTHER
6. NAPKIN
7. MELLOW
8. COMBAT
9. CANNON

PUZZLE #40
1. JOYOUS
2. ACHING
3. ATTACK
4. HAMMER
5. FATHOM
6. CUDDLE
7. POLICE
8. SHIFTY
9. ACTION

PUZZLE #41
1. CLOUDY
2. SUMMON
3. IMPACT
4. IMPEDE
5. UNWIND
6. TRENCH
7. MUSTER
8. UPHILL
9. ORPHAN

PUZZLE #42
1. DEFEAT
2. ANYONE
3. ACCEPT
4. INVITE
5. OBJECT
6. MINING
7. OFFEND
8. UNLESS
9. EXCESS

PUZZLE #43
1. INJURY
2. ACCUSE
3. ONWARD
4. IGNITE
5. CACTUS
6. UNEVEN
7. ALWAYS
8. OCTANE
9. OBLONG

PUZZLE #44
1. MISSUS
2. AMPERE
3. JALOPY
4. MARROW
5. CAMPER
6. CLUMPY
7. MUSLIN
8. PUNCHY
9. RUMPUS

PUZZLE #45
1. SQUIRM
2. ADROIT
3. CRAWLY
4. EQUATE
5. SEQUEL
6. TIDBIT
7. BISQUE
8. SCANTY
9. ABDUCT

PUZZLE #46
1. MARKET
2. ANKLET
3. DARKLY
4. HACKER
5. AVERSE
6. KILLER
7. EUREKA
8. BICKER
9. SHRUNK

PUZZLE #47
1. TOPPLE
2. ROTARY
3. WITHAL
4. THRONG
5. SAFETY
6. STYMIE
7. UNTOLD
8. SYNTAX
9. WINERY

PUZZLE #48
1. DOSAGE
2. ARGYLE
3. DEVOUR
4. TRIBAL
5. DAINTY
6. BIOPSY
7. BREACH
8. ENGULF
9. WIRING

PUZZLE #49
1. COFFIN
2. FACIAL
3. BEACON
4. DEFECT
5. FRISKY
6. SHIFTY
7. BISECT
8. COOKIE
9. ETHNIC

PUZZLE #50
1. BURGER
2. HOOPLA
3. SADDLE
4. POSTAL
5. FLINCH
6. LOAFER
7. TIDING
8. APLOMB
9. SLUDGE

PUZZLE #51
1. ANNUAL
2. FENCED
3. BLANCH
4. CARHOP
5. CLUMPY
6. DEFTLY
7. BOLERO
8. AFLAME
9. CAMPER

PUZZLE #52
1. CREASE
2. BOUNCY
3. ENSURE
4. DRAFTY
5. HAGGLE
6. ARCHED
7. WINERY
8. CAVORT
9. GRAINY

PUZZLE #53
1. JAILER
2. SEDUCE
3. MAGPIE
4. DEPOSE
5. CLIMAX
6. PRANCE
7. INLAND
8. ABDUCT
9. NESTLE

PUZZLE #54
1. DIVEST
2. CHERUB
3. SLOUGH
4. NUDIST
5. HERBAL
6. RADIUM
7. TEACUP
8. DERIVE
9. WORKED

PUZZLE #55
1. ARCHED
2. FRUITY
3. BISQUE
4. MARKED
5. CALLUS
6. APLOMB
7. SNEAKY
8. HACKLE
9. ESKIMO

ANSWERS

PUZZLE #56
1. GROCER
2. FRUGAL
3. LIMBER
4. BRIDLE
5. BECOME
6. KENNEL
7. CURSED
8. DETAIL
9. INFORM

PUZZLE #57
1. MERGE
2. HILLY
3. GROVE
4. EXHALE
5. HANGAR
6. GRAVEL
7. VISUAL
8. FOURTH
9. GAZEBO

PUZZLE #58
1. ALPHA
2. HOARD
3. LOCAL
4. WEIGHT
5. FICKLE
6. SAVAGE
7. WIRING
8. WRENCH
9. AIRWAY

PUZZLE #59
1. VERSUS
2. HOOPLA
3. GROCER
4. GERBIL
5. WINERY
6. DROWSY
7. HUMANE
8. HUNTED
9. EMBARK

PUZZLE #60
1. MYSELF
2. PELLET
3. RARELY
4. UNHOOK
5. SCURVY
6. RUNOFF
7. MORALE
8. SLOUGH
9. PUFFIN

PUZZLE #61
1. SYMBOL
2. THROWN
3. IMPEDE
4. FREELY
5. COTTON
6. FIXATE
7. HUMANE
8. DEPLOY
9. CRABBY

PUZZLE #62
1. TWELVE
2. JUNIOR
3. ARCTIC
4. CRYING
5. ESKIMO
6. LOCKET
7. MAYHEM
8. REVERT
9. UNRULY

PUZZLE #63
1. HALVES
2. SWIVEL
3. JESTER
4. NAUGHT
5. LOCKED
6. KIBOSH
7. ISOBAR
8. ATOMIC
9. MEEKLY

PUZZLE #64
1. BREACH
2. GALLOP
3. FRUGAL
4. BRAZEN
5. FLAWED
6. FREEZE
7. GUSHER
8. BRIGHT
9. CASUAL

PUZZLE #65
1. SUNKEN
2. VICTIM
3. OUTAGE
4. PICNIC
5. SAVING
6. SAFETY
7. BEACON
8. AMOUNT
9. SHRUNK

PUZZLE #66
1. INVEST
2. NOVICE
3. OBJECT
4. BOXING
5. ANNUAL
6. BRONCO
7. BICKER
8. TROPHY
9. INVITE

PUZZLE #67
1. GALLON
2. IRRUPT
3. INFANT
4. METRIC
5. OBLONG
6. SOCCER
7. BUSHEL
8. CORNER
9. BOTANY

PUZZLE #68
1. COARSE
2. TARGET
3. BROKEN
4. LETTER
5. COLLIE
6. AUTUMN
7. BARREL
8. POCKET
9. BETTER

PUZZLE #69
1. ASSIGN
2. OBTUSE
3. COLUMN
4. MATRIX
5. KITTEN
6. SHRIMP
7. JUGGLE
8. STUDIO
9. RELATE

PUZZLE #70
1. BUCKLE
2. BUTTER
3. TRENCH
4. RUDDER
5. BETTER
6. TETHER
7. WIZARD
8. PURSUE
9. ATOMIC

PUZZLE #71
1. ABSENT
2. INVEST
3. GRIEVE
4. SCHOOL
5. ZIPPER
6. INHALE
7. UNFAIR
8. ORANGE
9. BULLET

PUZZLE #72
1. GRITTY
2. FLABBY
3. IGNITE
4. HOMELY
5. AFGHAN
6. LIQUOR
7. ARGUER
8. GRISLY
9. HANGAR

PUZZLE #73
1. BALKED
2. EMBLEM
3. HORRID
4. AUBURN
5. DEMEAN
6. EXHUME
7. BALSAM
8. AMBUSH
9. HUMBLE

PUZZLE #74
1. ATOMIC
2. BENDER
3. MORALE
4. CLAMOR
5. BYWORD
6. MASKED
7. AMBUSH
8. BRIDLE
9. AWAKEN

PUZZLE #75
1. AVIATE
2. OUTAGE
3. WHEEZE
4. TWELVE
5. HAVING
6. PLACID
7. VICTIM
8. PROVEN
9. ZIPPER

ANSWERS

PUZZLE #76
1. JOSTLE
2. SWIVEL
3. IMPISH
4. SHELVE
5. TONSIL
6. RAVISH
7. SOCKET
8. PURITY
9. JOVIAL

PUZZLE #77
1. DRIVER
2. ANYONE
3. SINGLY
4. FRENZY
5. ARGYLE
6. NEATLY
7. GERBIL
8. DOCKET
9. JOYOUS

PUZZLE #78
1. SPONGY
2. ARGUER
3. GIBBER
4. BURGER
5. NUTMEG
6. CLERGY
7. NEGATE
8. AIMING
9. HIGHLY

PUZZLE #79
1. SHRIMP
2. SHIELD
3. PROFIT
4. RAFFLE
5. DROOPY
6. REVERT
7. SAVORY
8. FEWEST
9. DROWSY

PUZZLE #80
1. GROOVY
2. DEFECT
3. KNIGHT
4. COUGAR
5. LENGTH
6. CLINIC
7. KITTEN
8. GROWTH
9. DIVINE

PUZZLE #81
1. FIDDLE
2. LAVISH
3. ENROLL
4. EFFORT
5. INCOME
6. INSIST
7. FICKLE
8. GATHER
9. LENGTH

PUZZLE #82
1. PADDLE
2. POTENT
3. FELLOW
4. TRIPLE
5. NUMBER
6. NEPHEW
7. TEACUP
8. PACKET
9. SKETCH

PUZZLE #83
1. VOLUME
2. THROWN
3. WORTHY
4. ADVICE
5. ANNUAL
6. TYRANT
7. WANTED
8. VOICED
9. TRAUMA

PUZZLE #84
1. BANDIT
2. ANYONE
3. MINGLE
4. FORMAT
5. CHATTY
6. CANNON
7. MOVING
8. FUMBLE
9. AGENCY

PUZZLE #85
1. PURPLE
2. SAFARI
3. MODEST
4. BREEZY
5. BUCKLE
6. ROCKET
7. REFUSE
8. PUDDLE
9. MOSTLY

PUZZLE #86
1. BLURRY
2. EMBLEM
3. FONDLY
4. PRETTY
5. CUDDLE
6. COUNTY
7. COYOTE
8. ENSURE
9. BOTANY

PUZZLE #87
1. RUNNER
2. GOSSIP
3. PRANCE
4. GRUMPY
5. SCULPT
6. HAPPEN
7. SALARY
8. REVERT
9. PIRACY

PUZZLE #88
1. GLANCE
2. MUFFIN
3. LAVISH
4. NAPKIN
5. PASTRY
6. MANNER
7. MUMBLE
8. KETTLE
9. GOVERN

PUZZLE #89
1. OPPOSE
2. SHADOW
3. SAILOR
4. PICKUP
5. BEATEN
6. AUTHOR
7. ONWARD
8. BASKET
9. APIECE

PUZZLE #90
1. ANNUAL
2. CHOOSE
3. LUNACY
4. RADIUS
5. CLOSET
6. TRIPLE
7. DOLLAR
8. BLURRY
9. AFFECT